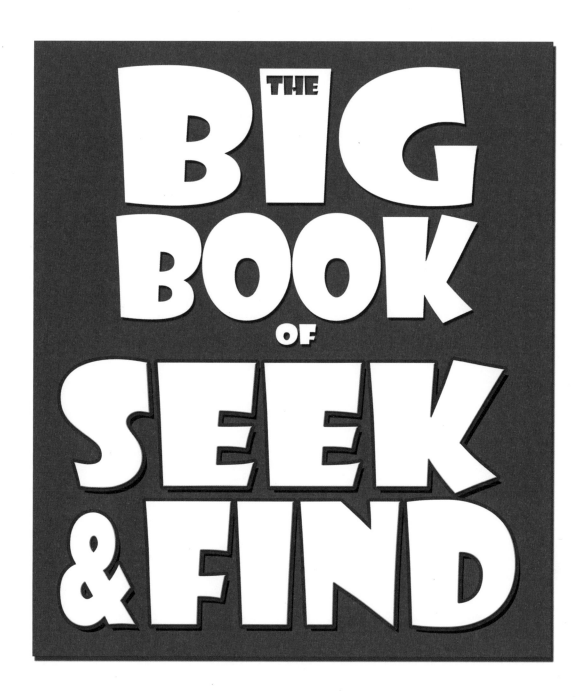

THE BIG BOOK OF SEEK & FIND

Tony Tallarico

Kidsbooks®

Visit us at www.kidsbooks.com®

"I wonder where we are," said Apatosaurus. "Why don't we split up and check it out?" They agreed, and decided to meet back at the cave at the end of their adventurous day. Can you find Apatosaurus at this carnival, along with the other fun things listed below?

- ☒ Alarm clock
- ☒ Apple
- ☒ Axe
- ☒ Bell
- ☒ Bones (2)
- ☒ Butterfly
- ☒ Candle
- ☒ Chef
- ☒ Crayon
- ☒ Elephant
- ☒ Ghost
- ☒ Hammock
- ☒ Knight
- ☒ Mice (3)
- ☒ Paintbrush
- ☒ Paint bucket
- ☒ Pencil
- ☒ Piano keys
- ☒ Skull
- ☒ Snake
- ☒ Snowman
- ☒ Stilts
- ☒ Turtle
- ☒ TV antennas (2)
- ☒ Two-headed alien
- ☒ Unicorn

"Oh, cool! But where am I?" said Triceratops *(try-SER-uh-tops)*. "Hey! I see some of my friends." Can you find Apatosaurus, Triceratops, and Compsognathus at this skating rink? Don't forget to look for the following fun things, too.

- Alligator
- Bone
- Bowling ball
- Broom
- Cactuses (2)
- Cameras (2)
- Crutch
- Elf
- Football player
- Humpty Dumpty
- Hungry monster
- Ice skateboard
- Igloo
- Kangaroo
- Lost mitten
- Mouse
- Necklace
- Panda
- Penguins (2)
- Pillow
- Roller skates
- Santa Claus
- Shark fin
- Skier
- Straw basket
- Telescope
- Television

"Yum! Something smells good," said Iguanodon *(ih-GWAHN-uh-don)*. "Maybe I'll give up eating plants." Can you find Apatosaurus, Triceratops, Compsognathus, and Iguanodon at this fast-food stand? Don't forget to look for the following fun things, too.

- ☑ Apple
- ☑ Astronaut
- ☑ Candy cane
- ☑ Chicken
- ☑ Clown
- ☑ Count Dracula
- ☑ Diver
- ☑ Doctor
- ☑ Dog

- ☐ Doughnut
- ☑ Duck
- ☐ Fish
- ☑ Monster
- ☑ Moose head
- ☐ Mouse
- ☑ Moustache
- ☐ Penguin
- ☑ Pinocchio

- ☑ Propeller
- ☑ Seal
- ☑ Star
- ☑ Straws (2)
- ☑ Surfer
- ☑ Torn bag
- ☑ Turtle
- ☑ Unicycle
- ☑ Viking

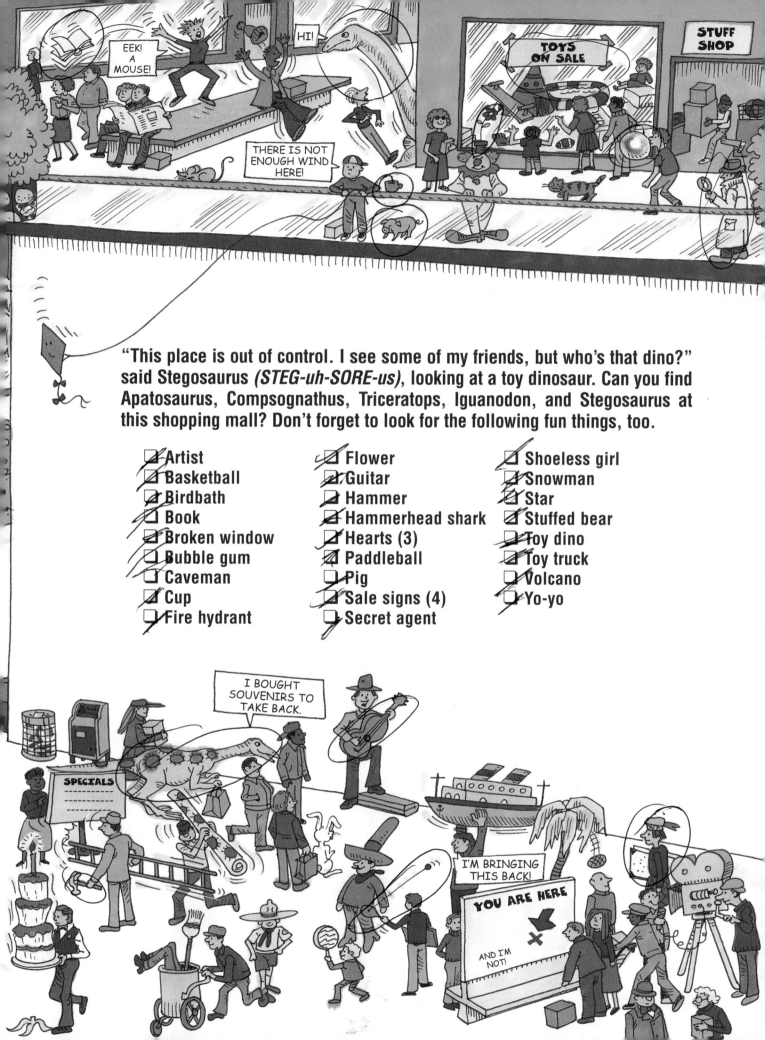

"This place is out of control. I see some of my friends, but who's that dino?" said Stegosaurus *(STEG-uh-SORE-us)*, looking at a toy dinosaur. Can you find Apatosaurus, Compsognathus, Triceratops, Iguanodon, and Stegosaurus at this shopping mall? Don't forget to look for the following fun things, too.

- Artist
- Basketball
- Birdbath
- Book
- Broken window
- Bubble gum
- Caveman
- Cup
- Fire hydrant
- Flower
- Guitar
- Hammer
- Hammerhead shark
- Hearts (3)
- Paddleball
- Pig
- Sale signs (4)
- Secret agent
- Shoeless girl
- Snowman
- Star
- Stuffed bear
- Toy dino
- Toy truck
- Volcano
- Yo-yo

"Look at all those little creatures! They seem to know where they're going," said Diplodocus *(dih-PLOH-duh-kus)*. "Maybe they can tell me where I am." Can you find Apatosaurus, Compsognathus, Triceratops, Iguanodon, Stegosaurus, and Diplodocus? Don't forget to look for the following fun things, too.

- ☐ Airplane
- ☐ Apple
- ☐ Arrow
- ☐ Balloons (3)
- ☐ Baseball
- ☐ Calendar
- ☐ Carrot
- ☐ Cat
- ☐ Coonskin cap
- ☐ Crown
- ☐ Elephant
- ☐ Football helmet
- ☐ Golf club
- ☐ Hockey stick
- ☐ Kites (2)
- ☐ Lunch box
- ☐ Oilcan
- ☐ Pyramid
- ☐ Rocket ship
- ☐ Roller skate
- ☐ Sailor hat
- ☐ Scissors
- ☐ Straw
- ☐ Unicorn
- ☐ Van
- ☐ Watering can

"I don't like this place at all," said Deinonychus *(dyne-ON-ik-us)*. "There are too many strange creatures. I'm getting out of here quick." Can you find Apatosaurus, Triceratops, Compsognathus, Iguanodon, Stegosaurus, Diplodocus, Coelophysis, and Deinonychus at this zoo? Don't forget to look for the following fun things, too.

- ❑ Aardvark
- ❑ Alien
- ❑ Anteater
- ❑ Arrow
- ❑ Baseball glove
- ❑ Bat
- ❑ Beaver
- ❑ Bighorn
- ❑ Bottle
- ❑ Butterfly
- ❑ Candle
- ❑ Clown

- ❑ Dog
- ❑ Duck
- ❑ Kangaroo
- ❑ Lost balloon
- ❑ Moose
- ❑ Net
- ❑ Owls (2)
- ❑ Panda
- ❑ Polar bear
- ❑ Raccoon

- ❑ Rhinoceros
- ❑ Sick animal
- ❑ Singing cactus
- ❑ Snakes (2)
- ❑ Toucan
- ❑ Umbrellas (3)
- ❑ Wolf
- ❑ Yak

I LIKE TO YIKKITY YAK... I'M A YAK!!

I LIVE HERE, TOO... I'M A TOUCAN.

THE EAGLE IS LANDING!

WHAT'S A BEAR DOING ON A SKATEBOARD?

SAY "AAAH!"

I'M A BIGHORN.

WHAT AM I DOING HERE?

I QUIT!

I HAVE A SORE THROAT.

I'M ON VACATION.

I'M AN AARDVARK... AND I'M THE FIRST ONE TO FIND ON THE LIST.

CUTE.

I'M KING OF THIS ZOO!

WHY NOT?

FOR RENT

"Oh, wow! What are those things flying in the air?" wondered Ankylosaurus *(an-KYE-low-SORE-us)*. Can you find Apatosaurus, Compsognathus, Triceratops, Iguanodon, Stegosaurus, Diplodocus, Coelophysis, Deinonychus, Tyrannosaurus, and Ankylosaurus at this big-balloon parade? Don't forget to look for the following fun things, too.

- ❏ Birds (2)
- ❏ Broom
- ❏ Candy cane
- ❏ Clown
- ❏ Coffeepot
- ❏ Cooking pot
- ❏ Cow
- ❏ Deflated balloon
- ❏ Fire hydrant
- ❏ Fish

- ❏ Giant
- ❏ Hammer
- ❏ Happy stars (5)
- ❏ Humpty Dumpty
- ❏ Ice skates (2 pairs)
- ❏ King Kong
- ❏ Kite
- ❏ Knight
- ❏ Lion
- ❏ Mouse
- ❏ Mummy
- ❏ Paintbrush

- ❏ Penguin
- ❏ Pirate
- ❏ Rabbits (2)
- ❏ Scarecrow
- ❏ Skier
- ❏ Sore feet
- ❏ Three Little Pigs
- ❏ Turtles (2)
- ❏ Unicyclist

Freddie and Lisa have discovered a house that is unlike any other—a haunted house!

FIND FREDDIE & LISA AT THE HAUNTED HOUSE, AND THESE FUN ITEMS:

- ❏ Apples (2)
- ❏ Baseball cap
- ❏ Bones (3)
- ❏ Box
- ❏ Burned-out candle
- ❏ Clothespin
- ❏ Coffeepot
- ❏ Crown
- ❏ Dog
- ❏ Duck
- ❏ Eyeglasses
- ❏ Faucet
- ❏ Fish tank
- ❏ Ghosts (3)
- ❏ Hammer
- ❏ Heart
- ❏ Kite
- ❏ Lips
- ❏ Mouse
- ❏ Owl
- ❏ Paint bucket
- ❏ Peanut
- ❏ Pencils (2)
- ❏ Piggy bank
- ❏ Saw
- ❏ Sock
- ❏ Submarine
- ❏ Truck
- ❏ Umbrella

Should they go in?
Should they stay in?
What do you think they
should do?

**FIND FREDDIE & LISA
BEFORE THEY DECIDE,
AND THESE FUN ITEMS:**

- ❑ Birds (2)
- ❑ Blimps (2)
- ❑ Bowling ball
- ❑ Broom
- ❑ Camel
- ❑ Candle
- ❑ Chef's hat
- ❑ Feather
- ❑ Flower
- ❑ Football
- ❑ Giraffe
- ❑ Jester
- ❑ King
- ❑ Laundry
- ❑ Lost boot
- ❑ Moustache
- ❑ Napoleon
- ❑ Painted egg
- ❑ Rabbit
- ❑ Red wagon
- ❑ Sailboat
- ❑ Short pants
- ❑ Skull
- ❑ Sled
- ❑ Slide
- ❑ Star
- ❑ Top hats (2)
- ❑ Trash can
- ❑ Umbrella

Ready, set, go! Everyone runs toward the door of the haunted house, but only two enter it!

FIND FREDDIE & LISA AS THEY MEET THE MONSTERS, AND THESE FUN ITEMS:
- ❏ Apple
- ❏ Arrow
- ❏ Bag
- ❏ Balloon
- ❏ Banana peel
- ❏ Baseball cap
- ❏ Bone
- ❏ Boot
- ❏ Broken heart
- ❏ Broom
- ❏ Cake
- ❏ Candles (5)
- ❏ Crystal ball
- ❏ Fish
- ❏ Genie
- ❏ Ghosts (2)
- ❏ Ice-cream cone
- ❏ Lightning
- ❏ Necktie
- ❏ Owl
- ❏ Piano
- ❏ Skulls (5)
- ❏ Snake
- ❏ Spoon
- ❏ Tombstone

Ms. Witch makes gross snacks. Her specialty is the "Everything Goes" sandwich!

FIND FREDDIE & LISA AT SNACK TIME, AND THESE FUN ITEMS:

- ❏ Accordion
- ❏ Apple
- ❏ Baseball
- ❏ Blackbird
- ❏ Bone
- ❏ Candle
- ❏ Checkerboard
- ❏ Drill
- ❏ Earring
- ❏ Fish (2)
- ❏ Flower
- ❏ Fork
- ❏ Frying pan
- ❏ Grapes
- ❏ Green cup
- ❏ Heart
- ❏ Helmet
- ❏ Ice-cream cone
- ❏ Ladle
- ❏ Neckties (2)
- ❏ Oilcan
- ❏ Orange
- ❏ Palm tree
- ❏ Pear
- ❏ Rolling pin
- ❏ Saw
- ❏ Sock
- ❏ Stool
- ❏ Toaster
- ❏ Wooden spoon

Freddie and Lisa begin to explore the haunted house. A wrong turn, and down they tumble!

FIND FREDDIE & LISA IN THE DUNGEON, AND THESE FUN ITEMS:

- ❏ Airplane
- ❏ Balloon
- ❏ Banana peel
- ❏ Bowling ball
- ❏ Broken egg
- ❏ Broom
- ❏ Candy cane
- ❏ Corn
- ❏ Cupcake
- ❏ Doctor
- ❏ Drum
- ❏ Fire hydrant
- ❏ Flowerpot
- ❏ Flying bat
- ❏ Football
- ❏ Hot dog
- ❏ Ice-cream cone
- ❏ Ice-cream pop
- ❏ Mummies (3)
- ❏ Piggy bank
- ❏ Rabbit
- ❏ Roller skates
- ❏ Scarecrow
- ❏ Shark
- ❏ Skateboard
- ❏ Skulls (2)
- ❏ Skunk
- ❏ Top hat
- ❏ Umbrellas (2)
- ❏ Wagon

Next to the dungeon are the wildest lanes in town. It's a great place to do anything—but bowl!

FIND FREDDIE & LISA AT THE GHOSTLY BOWLING ALLEY, AND THESE FUN ITEMS:

- ❑ Arrow
- ❑ Balloon
- ❑ Bird
- ❑ Bodiless head
- ❑ Broken ball
- ❑ Broom
- ❑ Cactus
- ❑ Candles (2)
- ❑ Carrot
- ❑ Dog
- ❑ Earphones
- ❑ Flower
- ❑ Hamburger
- ❑ Hot dog
- ❑ Mouse
- ❑ Mummy
- ❑ Mummy's ball
- ❑ Orange
- ❑ Pear
- ❑ Periscope
- ❑ Robot
- ❑ Sailboat
- ❑ Snowman
- ❑ Spring
- ❑ Sunglasses (2 pairs)
- ❑ Sword
- ❑ Tennis racket
- ❑ Tombstone
- ❑ Yo-yo

Dr. Frankenstein has lots of patients who need lots of patience.

FIND FREDDIE & LISA IN DR. FRANKENSTEIN'S LABORATORY, AND THESE FUN ITEMS:

- ❑ Black cat
- ❑ Book
- ❑ Bride
- ❑ Bunny fiend
- ❑ Candle
- ❑ Cheese
- ❑ Dog
- ❑ Dracula
- ❑ Duck
- ❑ Feather
- ❑ Greeting card
- ❑ Ice-cream pop
- ❑ Invisible person
- ❑ Paintbrush
- ❑ Paint bucket
- ❑ Pickax
- ❑ Roller skates
- ❑ Sailor fiend
- ❑ Saw
- ❑ Screwdriver
- ❑ Shovel
- ❑ Skull
- ❑ Suspenders
- ❑ Television
- ❑ Three-legged thing
- ❑ Toy block
- ❑ Tulip
- ❑ Two-headed thing
- ❑ Watch

After dinner, Freddie and Lisa explore a room upstairs. There they find someone who *really* knows how to save!

FIND FREDDIE & LISA IN DRACULA'S ATTIC, AND THESE FUN ITEMS:

- ❑ Boomerang
- ❑ Broom
- ❑ Candy cane
- ❑ Chef's hat
- ❑ Clocks (2)
- ❑ Cracked mirror
- ❑ Fire hydrant
- ❑ Garden hose
- ❑ Golf club
- ❑ Ice-cream cone
- ❑ Key
- ❑ Mouse
- ❑ Necklace
- ❑ Oar
- ❑ Paint bucket
- ❑ Paper airplane
- ❑ Pencil
- ❑ Pyramid
- ❑ Saw
- ❑ Skateboard
- ❑ Skulls (4)
- ❑ Slice of pizza
- ❑ Spray can
- ❑ Straw
- ❑ String of pearls
- ❑ Stuffed panda
- ❑ Telephone booth
- ❑ Viking helmet
- ❑ Yarn

The monsters walk very carefully when they visit *this* room!

FIND FREDDIE & LISA IN THE COBWEB ROOM, AND THESE FUN ITEMS:

- ❑ Baby carriage
- ❑ Binoculars
- ❑ Bow tie
- ❑ Boxing glove
- ❑ Broom
- ❑ Cup
- ❑ Dog
- ❑ Duck
- ❑ Earring
- ❑ Electric plug
- ❑ Fish
- ❑ Flower
- ❑ Football helmet
- ❑ Fork
- ❑ Ghosts (2)
- ❑ Hammer
- ❑ Heart
- ❑ Key
- ❑ Lock
- ❑ Mummy
- ❑ Old-fashioned radio
- ❑ Pencil
- ❑ Quarter moon
- ❑ Ring
- ❑ Robot
- ❑ Screwdriver
- ❑ Ship
- ❑ Skull
- ❑ Top hat
- ❑ Turtles (2)
- ❑ Wagon

Playtime for monsters!

FIND FREDDIE & LISA
IN THE MONSTERS'
PLAYROOM, AND
THESE FUN ITEMS:
- ☐ Artist
- ☐ Balloon
- ☐ Banana peel
- ☐ Barbell
- ☐ Birds (2)
- ☐ Blackboard
- ☐ Crayons (5)
- ☐ Donkey
- ☐ Fish
- ☐ Football
- ☐ Haunted house
- ☐ Hole in the head
- ☐ Hood
- ☐ Ice skate
- ☐ Jack-o'-lanterns (4)
- ☐ Joke book
- ☐ Juggler
- ☐ Mask
- ☐ Monster puppet
- ☐ Mummy doll
- ☐ Musician
- ☐ Nail
- ☐ Pail
- ☐ Pogo stick
- ☐ Rubber ducky
- ☐ Sailboat
- ☐ Snake
- ☐ Telephone
- ☐ Tricycle
- ☐ Turtle
- ☐ Wind-up monster

It is time for Freddie and Lisa to go. The friendly monsters hope their new friends will return soon.

FIND FREDDIE & LISA LEAVING THE HAUNTED HOUSE, AND THESE FUN ITEMS:

- ❏ Apple
- ❏ Arrow
- ❏ Balloon
- ❏ Birds (2)
- ❏ Box
- ❏ Broken heart
- ❏ Brooms (2)
- ❏ Candles (2)
- ❏ Clock
- ❏ Crown
- ❏ Dog
- ❏ Duck
- ❏ Envelope
- ❏ Flower
- ❏ Ice skates
- ❏ Key
- ❏ Ladder
- ❏ Lamp
- ❏ Mouse
- ❏ Painted egg
- ❏ Periscope
- ❏ Quarter moon
- ❏ Rabbit
- ❏ Roller skates
- ❏ Shovel
- ❏ Skull
- ❏ TV camera
- ❏ Umbrella

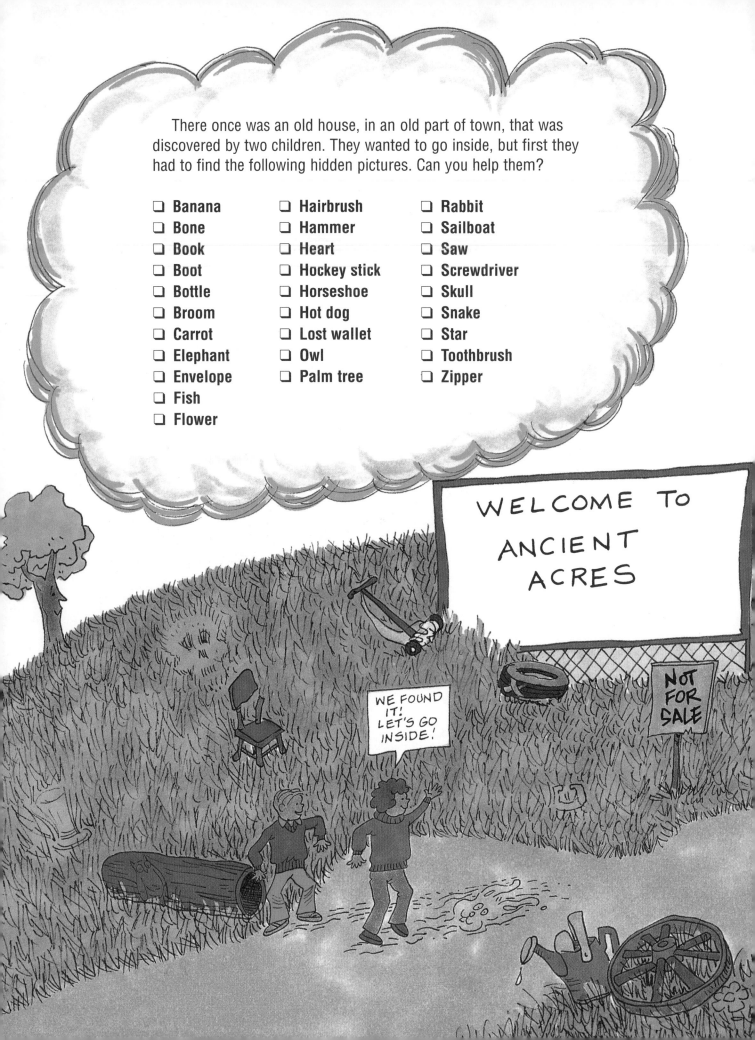

There once was an old house, in an old part of town, that was discovered by two children. They wanted to go inside, but first they had to find the following hidden pictures. Can you help them?

- Banana
- Bone
- Book
- Boot
- Bottle
- Broom
- Carrot
- Elephant
- Envelope
- Fish
- Flower

- Hairbrush
- Hammer
- Heart
- Hockey stick
- Horseshoe
- Hot dog
- Lost wallet
- Owl
- Palm tree

- Rabbit
- Sailboat
- Saw
- Screwdriver
- Skull
- Snake
- Star
- Toothbrush
- Zipper

WELCOME TO ANCIENT ACRES

WE FOUND IT! LET'S GO INSIDE!

NOT FOR SALE

In the old house was an old trunk, which the children opened with an old key. Out of the trunk came many strange things, including these hidden objects:

- ❏ Arrow
- ❏ Balloon
- ❏ Bearded man
- ❏ Carrot
- ❏ Chicken
- ❏ Fish
- ❏ Giraffe
- ❏ Horse
- ❏ Kite
- ❏ Mouse
- ❏ Quarter moon
- ❏ Snowman
- ❏ Tepee
- ❏ Tombstone
- ❏ Turtle
- ❏ Unicorn

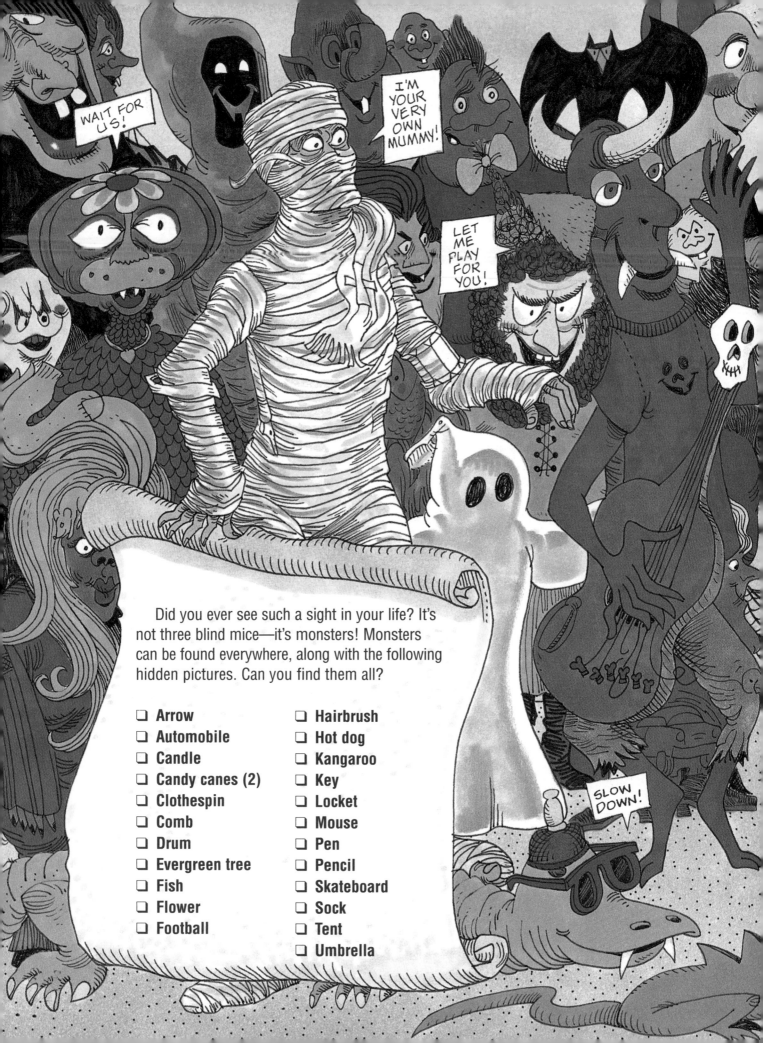

Did you ever see such a sight in your life? It's not three blind mice—it's monsters! Monsters can be found everywhere, along with the following hidden pictures. Can you find them all?

❑ Arrow
❑ Automobile
❑ Candle
❑ Candy canes (2)
❑ Clothespin
❑ Comb
❑ Drum
❑ Evergreen tree
❑ Fish
❑ Flower
❑ Football

❑ Hairbrush
❑ Hot dog
❑ Kangaroo
❑ Key
❑ Locket
❑ Mouse
❑ Pen
❑ Pencil
❑ Skateboard
❑ Sock
❑ Tent
❑ Umbrella

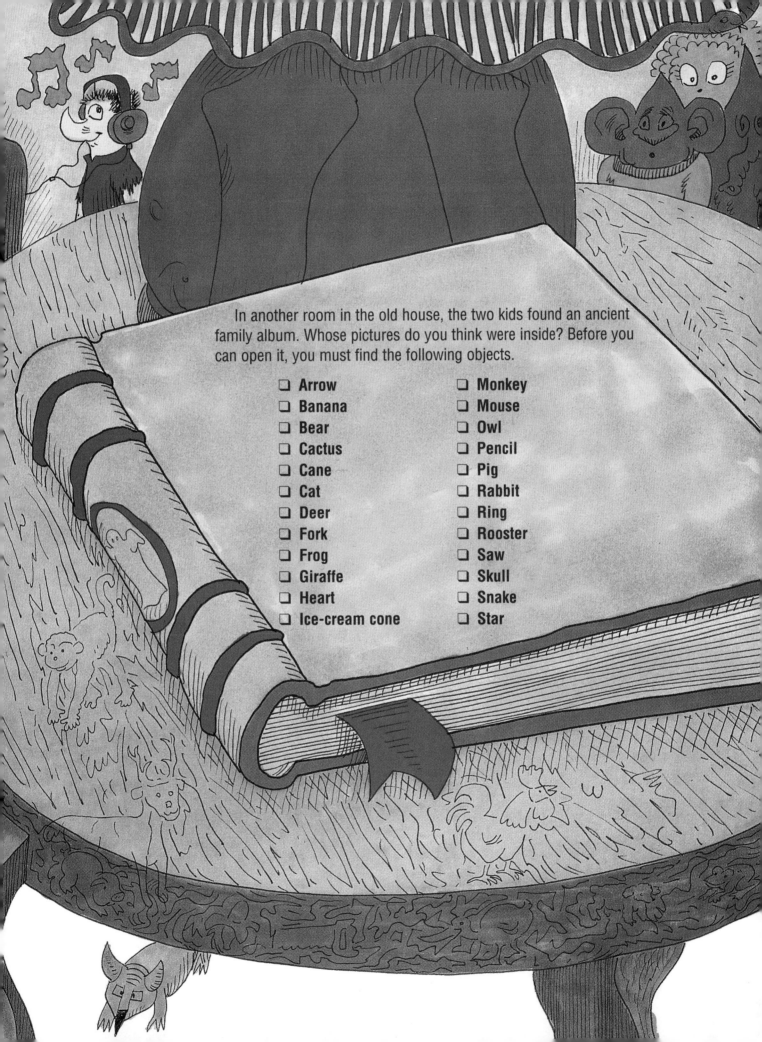

In another room in the old house, the two kids found an ancient family album. Whose pictures do you think were inside? Before you can open it, you must find the following objects.

- ❑ Arrow
- ❑ Banana
- ❑ Bear
- ❑ Cactus
- ❑ Cane
- ❑ Cat
- ❑ Deer
- ❑ Fork
- ❑ Frog
- ❑ Giraffe
- ❑ Heart
- ❑ Ice-cream cone
- ❑ Monkey
- ❑ Mouse
- ❑ Owl
- ❑ Pencil
- ❑ Pig
- ❑ Rabbit
- ❑ Ring
- ❑ Rooster
- ❑ Saw
- ❑ Skull
- ❑ Snake
- ❑ Star

Wow! What a surprise! It is a photo album full of monsters!
On the first page, there is a picture of young Frankenstein on
his first date. Do you know which monster is on the next page?
Before you look, find the following hidden objects:

- Airplane
- Automobile
- Butterfly
- Camera
- Candle
- Cup
- Drum
- Eyeglasses
- Fish

- Hearts (4)
- House
- Kite
- Lightbulb
- Owl
- Pencil
- Ring
- Rocket
- Sailboat

- Snake
- Surfboard
- Sword
- Tent
- Toothpaste
- Tree
- Turtle
- Umbrella
- Whistle

Wasn't Count Dracula a cuddly little critter? He loved to hide things. Can you find everything that he has hidden?

- ❏ Carrot
- ❏ Clown
- ❏ Coffeepot
- ❏ Comb
- ❏ Crown
- ❏ Elephant
- ❏ Fish
- ❏ Flashlight
- ❏ Flower

- ❏ Flying bats (10)
- ❏ Football
- ❏ Ghost
- ❏ Heart
- ❏ Hockey stick
- ❏ Hot dog
- ❏ Ice-cream cone
- ❏ Igloo
- ❏ Jack-o'-lantern

- ❏ Key
- ❏ Kite
- ❏ Mushroom
- ❏ Paintbrush
- ❏ Pencil
- ❏ Pizza
- ❏ Pyramid
- ❏ Sailor hat
- ❏ Top hat

This is the largest picture in the monster family album. It is the abominable snow kid building snow monsters. He has also thrown in some hidden pictures. Look closely to find them all.

- ❑ **Alligator**
- ❑ **Banana**
- ❑ **Bow tie**
- ❑ **Cactus**
- ❑ **Can**
- ❑ **Candle**
- ❑ **Cheese**
- ❑ **Chef's hat**
- ❑ **Cowboy hat**
- ❑ **Duck**
- ❑ **Fish**
- ❑ **Ghost**
- ❑ **Heart**
- ❑ **Hot dog**
- ❑ **Ice-cream cone**
- ❑ **Ice skate**
- ❑ **Ladder**
- ❑ **Lamp**
- ❑ **Lion**
- ❑ **Mouse**
- ❑ **Paintbrush**
- ❑ **Picture frame**
- ❑ **Pie**
- ❑ **Pig**
- ❑ **Pirate**
- ❑ **Shoe**
- ❑ **Shovel**
- ❑ **Top hat**
- ❑ **Umbrella**
- ❑ **Watering can**

Here is the mummy, showing off his childhood pictures. You sure can get wrapped up in them! You also can get wrapped up in looking for the following hidden objects.

- Apple
- Arrow
- Artist
- Bird
- Blimp
- Bone
- Book
- Cupcake
- Drum
- Fish
- Football
- Ghost
- Golf club
- Hammer
- Kangaroo
- Kite
- Owl
- Pinocchio
- Sailor hat
- Saw
- Scarecrow
- Wagon

These are really terrific pictures—the best in the album! They are, of course, pictures of the invisible man throughout the years. Try to find the following objects:

- ❑ Banana
- ❑ Basket
- ❑ Bone
- ❑ Carrot
- ❑ Cheese
- ❑ Evergreen tree
- ❑ Fire hydrant
- ❑ Football
- ❑ Graduate's hat
- ❑ Guitar
- ❑ Hamburger
- ❑ Heart
- ❑ Hot dog
- ❑ Ice-cream soda
- ❑ Lightbulb
- ❑ Mouse
- ❑ Pear
- ❑ Pencil
- ❑ Rose
- ❑ Screwdriver
- ❑ Shovel
- ❑ Snail
- ❑ Star
- ❑ Television
- ❑ Tent
- ❑ Turtle
- ❑ Unicorn

FIRST BIRTHDAY ⤸

KID LEAGUE STAR ⤸

FIRST DAY OF SCHOOL ⤸

INVISIBLE PAPER ⤴

SCHOOL FIELD TRIP

SOCCER CHAMP

TALKING TO SANTA

FIRST INVISIBLE MAN ON THE MOON

One picture is too big to fit into the album.
It's so big, it's hiding the following hidden pictures:

- ❏ Balloons (2)
- ❏ Birdhouse
- ❏ Birds (2)
- ❏ Boat
- ❏ Clock
- ❏ Coffeepot
- ❏ Covered wagon
- ❏ Crown
- ❏ Dog
- ❏ Elephant
- ❏ Fish (3)
- ❏ Hearts (2)
- ❏ Horseshoe
- ❏ Jack-o'-lantern
- ❏ Key
- ❏ Kite
- ❏ Mailbox
- ❏ Mermaid
- ❏ Old radio
- ❏ Old sock
- ❏ Old tire
- ❏ Pizza
- ❏ Tepee
- ❏ Worm

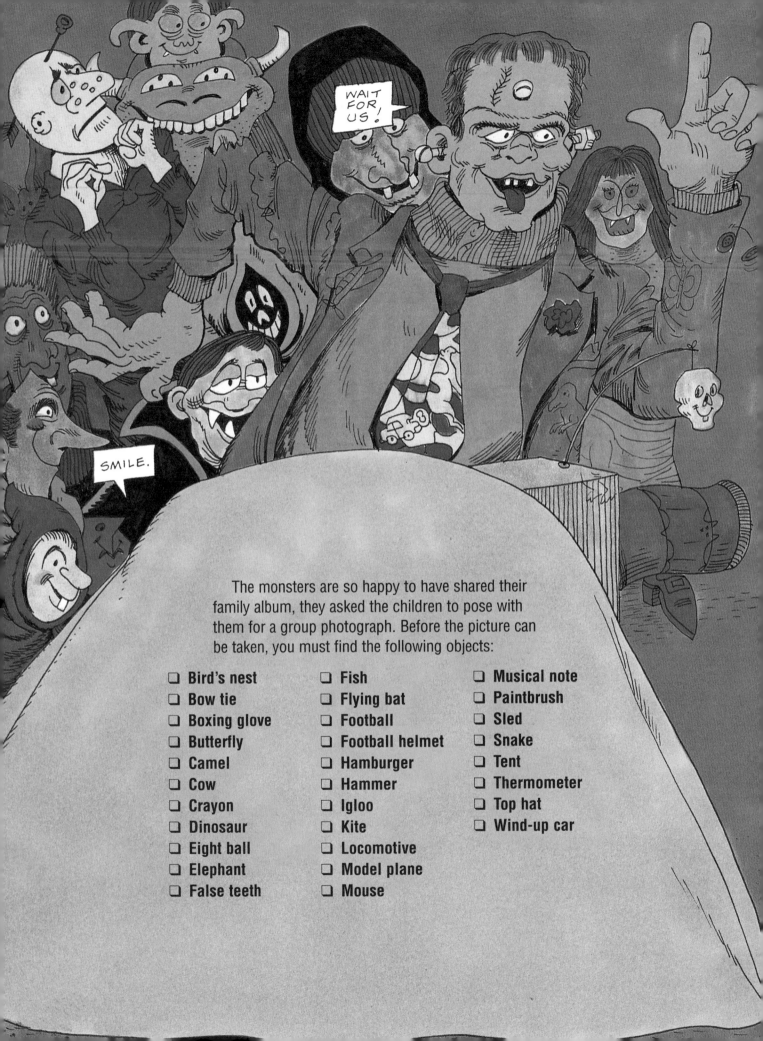

The monsters are so happy to have shared their family album, they asked the children to pose with them for a group photograph. Before the picture can be taken, you must find the following objects:

- Bird's nest
- Bow tie
- Boxing glove
- Butterfly
- Camel
- Cow
- Crayon
- Dinosaur
- Eight ball
- Elephant
- False teeth
- Fish
- Flying bat
- Football
- Football helmet
- Hamburger
- Hammer
- Igloo
- Kite
- Locomotive
- Model plane
- Mouse
- Musical note
- Paintbrush
- Sled
- Snake
- Tent
- Thermometer
- Top hat
- Wind-up car

Early one morning, Frankie has a brilliant idea. He decides to visit some friends he hasn't seen in a long time.

FIND FRANKIE IN HIS NUTTY NEIGHBORHOOD, AND THESE FUN ITEMS:

- ❑ Book
- ❑ Bowling ball
- ❑ Bucket
- ❑ Candle
- ❑ Dog
- ❑ Duck
- ❑ Fish (3)
- ❑ Flying bats (3)
- ❑ Football helmet
- ❑ Hammer
- ❑ Heart
- ❑ Jack-o'-lantern
- ❑ Moose head
- ❑ Periscope
- ❑ Pinocchio
- ❑ Raincoat
- ❑ Roller skates
- ❑ Sailor hat
- ❑ Scarecrow
- ❑ Skier
- ❑ Skull
- ❑ Star
- ❑ Tepee
- ❑ Thermometer
- ❑ Tulip
- ❑ Turtle
- ❑ Watering can
- ❑ Wreath

Frankie first looks for his old, old friend Manny Mummy in a place with lots of sand.

FIND MANNY MUMMY IN THE DRY DESERT, AND THESE FUN ITEMS:

- ❑ Balloons (3)
- ❑ Banana peel
- ❑ Bathtub
- ❑ Birdhouse
- ❑ Brooms (2)
- ❑ Earring
- ❑ Fire hydrant
- ❑ Fish (2)
- ❑ Flower
- ❑ Gas pump
- ❑ Ring
- ❑ Sailor hat
- ❑ Sand castle
- ❑ Sand pail
- ❑ Sled
- ❑ Slingshot
- ❑ Snake
- ❑ Snowman
- ❑ Soccer ball
- ❑ Star
- ❑ Straw
- ❑ Suitcase
- ❑ Surfboard
- ❑ Turtle
- ❑ TV antenna
- ❑ Umbrella
- ❑ Watering can
- ❑ Watermelon slice

Frankie and Manny Mummy set off to find their friend Batty Bat. He lives in a strange place.

FIND BATTY BAT IN TERRIFYING TRANSYLVANIA, AND THESE FUN ITEMS:

- ❏ Alligator
- ❏ Arrows (2)
- ❏ Baker
- ❏ Bones (6)
- ❏ Book
- ❏ Bride and groom
- ❏ Broken heart
- ❏ Broken mirror
- ❏ Candle
- ❏ Dog
- ❏ Fish
- ❏ Flower
- ❏ Football
- ❏ Fortune teller
- ❏ Hair dryer
- ❏ Kite
- ❏ Lion
- ❏ Mouse
- ❏ Nail
- ❏ Octopus
- ❏ Rabbit
- ❏ Scissors
- ❏ Skulls (4)
- ❏ Top hat
- ❏ Training wheels
- ❏ Umbrella
- ❏ Vulture
- ❏ Worm

Now they are off to find another pal. This one lives in a swamp!

FIND SWAMPY SAM IN THIS MUSHY MARSH, AND THESE FUN ITEMS:

- ❑ Apple
- ❑ Cupcake
- ❑ Drum
- ❑ Football helmet
- ❑ Fork
- ❑ Frog
- ❑ Grand piano
- ❑ Hammer
- ❑ Key
- ❑ Lost boot
- ❑ Lost mitten
- ❑ Medal
- ❑ Moon face
- ❑ Necktie
- ❑ Palm tree
- ❑ Pencil
- ❑ Pizza slice
- ❑ Ring
- ❑ Snake
- ❑ Soccer ball
- ❑ Sock
- ❑ Speaker
- ❑ Spoon
- ❑ Toothbrush
- ❑ Trumpet
- ❑ Umbrellas (2)

Warren Werewolf is Frankie's next friend to find. He plays baseball with the Dead End Dodgers.

FIND WARREN WEREWOLF AT THE BALLPARK, AND THESE FUN ITEMS:

- ❑ Bicycle horn
- ❑ Bone
- ❑ Cactus
- ❑ Candy cane
- ❑ Carrot
- ❑ Cookie
- ❑ Crown
- ❑ Empty can
- ❑ Eyeglasses (2)
- ❑ Feather
- ❑ Fir tree
- ❑ Flamingo
- ❑ Footprint
- ❑ Frog
- ❑ Heart
- ❑ Horseshoe
- ❑ Humpty Dumpty
- ❑ Kite
- ❑ Lamp
- ❑ Pliers
- ❑ Six-fingered glove
- ❑ Skull
- ❑ Squirrel
- ❑ Tic-tac-toe
- ❑ Witch
- ❑ Worm

Frankie and his pals go to an old school-house, where their friend Lena Lightning is a student.

FIND LENA LIGHTNING AMONG HER CREEPY CLASSMATES, AND THESE FUN ITEMS:

- ❑ Apple core
- ❑ Bell
- ❑ Bone tree
- ❑ Broken mirror
- ❑ Cactus
- ❑ Candles (3)
- ❑ Crystal ball
- ❑ Egg
- ❑ Firecracker
- ❑ Flashlight
- ❑ Flying bats (3)
- ❑ Fortune teller
- ❑ Hot dog
- ❑ Ice skate
- ❑ Mask
- ❑ Mouse
- ❑ Necktie
- ❑ Owl
- ❑ Pencil
- ❑ Saw
- ❑ Shark fin
- ❑ Skateboard
- ❑ Skunk
- ❑ Snakes (2)
- ❑ Star
- ❑ Vulture
- ❑ Worm

Next, Frankie and his friends set out to visit Greta Ghost, but none of her neighbors has seen her in a while.

FIND FRANKIE AND HIS OTHER FRIENDS AT GRETA'S HAUNTED HOUSE, AND THESE FUN ITEMS:

- ❏ Alligator
- ❏ Arrows (2)
- ❏ Axe
- ❏ Balloons (5)
- ❏ Banana peel
- ❏ Bowling ball
- ❏ Broom
- ❏ Cup
- ❏ Dart
- ❏ Drum
- ❏ Fork
- ❏ Hammer
- ❏ Hatched egg
- ❏ Heart
- ❏ Keys (2)
- ❏ Ring
- ❏ Screwdriver
- ❏ Ski
- ❏ Stool
- ❏ Sword
- ❏ Teapot
- ❏ Tepee
- ❏ Torn sock
- ❏ Turtle
- ❏ Umbrella
- ❏ Wreath

Frankie can't find Greta Ghost at the haunted house, so he and his friends check the new condos.

FIND GRETA GHOST IN MODERN MONSTERVILLE, AND THESE FUN ITEMS:

- ❏ Arrow
- ❏ Balloons (4)
- ❏ Bones (2)
- ❏ Camel
- ❏ Candles (3)
- ❏ Fire hydrant
- ❏ Fish (3)
- ❏ Flowers (3)
- ❏ Football helmet
- ❏ Frog
- ❏ Hoe
- ❏ Horseshoe
- ❏ Ice-cream cone
- ❏ Igloo
- ❏ Kites (2)
- ❏ Lollipop
- ❏ Lost bathing trunks
- ❏ Lost boot
- ❏ Mice (3)
- ❏ Painted egg
- ❏ Periscope
- ❏ Pyramid
- ❏ Quarter moon
- ❏ Rabbit
- ❏ Roller skates
- ❏ Sea horse
- ❏ Seal
- ❏ Sunglasses (2)

Together at last, the friends go on a picnic—where else but in a cemetery?

FIND FRANKIE AND HIS FRIENDS IN THIS GHOULISH GRAVEYARD, AND THESE FUN ITEMS:

- ❏ Apron
- ❏ Baseball cap
- ❏ Broom
- ❏ Bucket
- ❏ Burned-out candle
- ❏ Chef's hat
- ❏ Clothespin
- ❏ Crown
- ❏ Fish (2)
- ❏ Flower
- ❏ Guitar
- ❏ Heart
- ❏ House
- ❏ Lightbulb
- ❏ Mice (2)
- ❏ Paintbrush
- ❏ Picture frame
- ❏ Pig
- ❏ Ring
- ❏ Shovel
- ❏ Spoon
- ❏ Straw
- ❏ Tire
- ❏ Truck
- ❏ TV antenna
- ❏ Worm
- ❏ Wristwatch

After the picnic, Frankie and his friends go to see—you guessed it!—a monster movie.

FIND FRANKIE AND HIS FRIENDS AT THIS FRIGHTENING FLICK, AND THESE FUN ITEMS:

- ❑ Apple core
- ❑ Arrow
- ❑ Crown
- ❑ Dog
- ❑ Drum
- ❑ Eight ball
- ❑ Eyeglasses
- ❑ Faucet
- ❑ Fish skeleton
- ❑ Flashlight
- ❑ Fortune teller
- ❑ Heart
- ❑ Ice-cream pop
- ❑ Necktie
- ❑ Oilcan
- ❑ Paper airplane
- ❑ Periscope
- ❑ Piggy bank
- ❑ Rabbit
- ❑ Roller skates
- ❑ Sailboat
- ❑ Skunk
- ❑ Star
- ❑ Superhero
- ❑ Toast
- ❑ Top hat
- ❑ Trash can
- ❑ Trumpet
- ❑ Worm

While walking back from the movie, Frankie and his friends see a frightening sight!

FIND FRANKIE AND HIS FRIENDS WITH THESE TERRIFIC TRICK-OR-TREATERS, AND THESE FUN ITEMS:

- ❑ Balloon
- ❑ Broom
- ❑ Butterfly
- ❑ Candy cane
- ❑ Carrot
- ❑ Chef's hat
- ❑ Crown
- ❑ Earmuffs
- ❑ Fork
- ❑ Key
- ❑ Moustache
- ❑ Paintbrush
- ❑ Paper bag
- ❑ Pencil
- ❑ Pizza
- ❑ Roller skates
- ❑ Sailor hat
- ❑ Sock
- ❑ Star
- ❑ Top hat
- ❑ Tree ornament
- ❑ Umbrella
- ❑ Watering can
- ❑ Worm

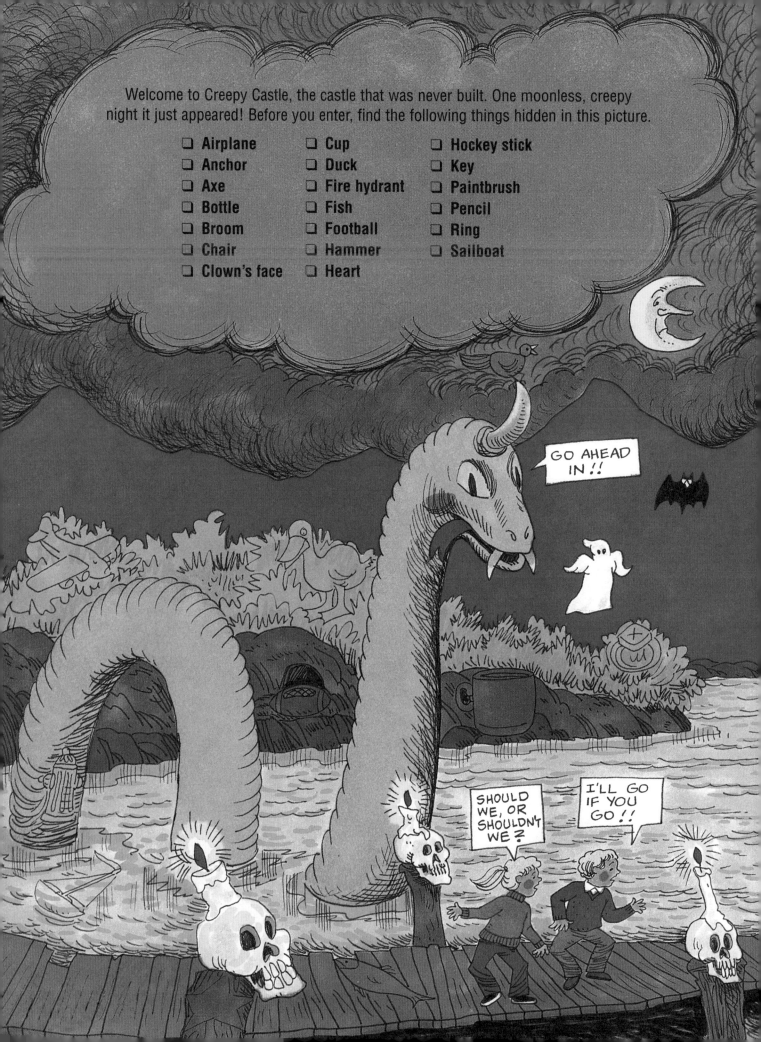

Welcome to Creepy Castle, the castle that was never built. One moonless, creepy night it just appeared! Before you enter, find the following things hidden in this picture.

- Airplane
- Anchor
- Axe
- Bottle
- Broom
- Chair
- Clown's face
- Cup
- Duck
- Fire hydrant
- Fish
- Football
- Hammer
- Heart
- Hockey stick
- Key
- Paintbrush
- Pencil
- Ring
- Sailboat

WELCOME?

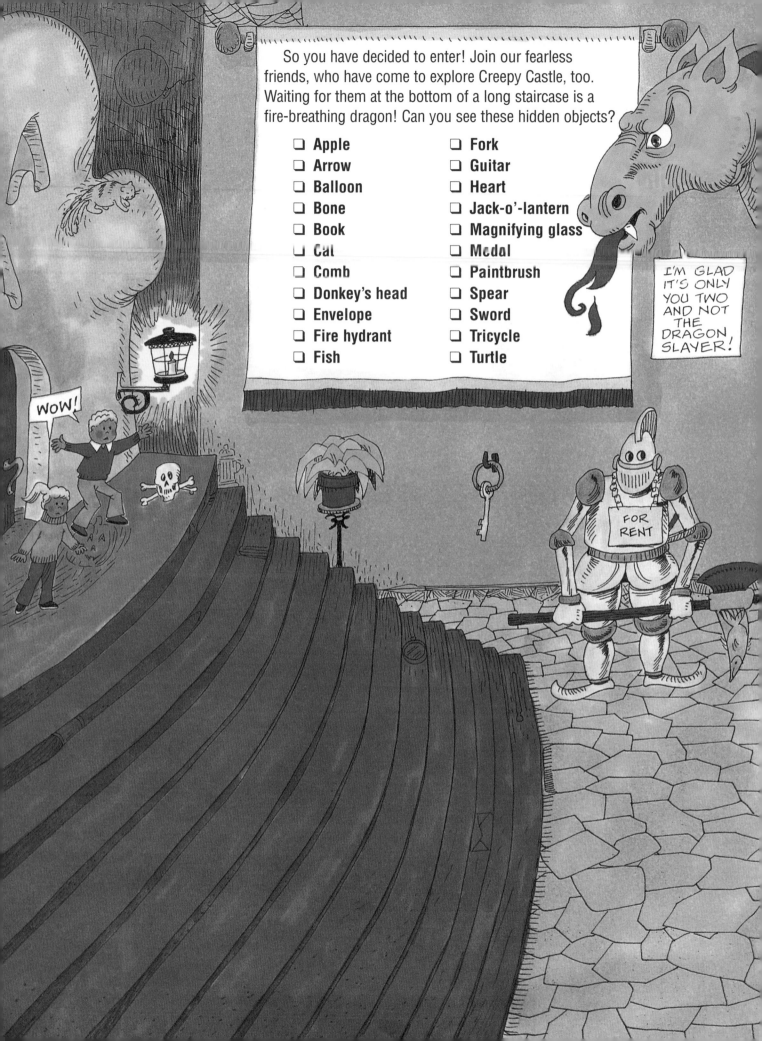

So you have decided to enter! Join our fearless friends, who have come to explore Creepy Castle, too. Waiting for them at the bottom of a long staircase is a fire-breathing dragon! Can you see these hidden objects?

- Apple
- Arrow
- Balloon
- Bone
- Book
- Cat
- Comb
- Donkey's head
- Envelope
- Fire hydrant
- Fish
- Fork
- Guitar
- Heart
- Jack-o'-lantern
- Magnifying glass
- Medal
- Paintbrush
- Spear
- Sword
- Tricycle
- Turtle

Now here is a weird sight—a headless knight! Could he be related to the Headless Horseman of Sleepy Hollow? Before going on, find these hidden pictures.

❑ Baseball bat
❑ Book
❑ Bottle
❑ Cow's head
❑ Cupcake
❑ Duck
❑ Eagle's head
❑ Ear of corn
❑ Envelope
❑ Feather
❑ Frog

❑ Ghost
❑ Hot dog
❑ Key
❑ Paper clip
❑ Pea pod
❑ Saw
❑ Shoe
❑ Toothbrush
❑ Turtle
❑ Umbrella
❑ Wheelbarrow

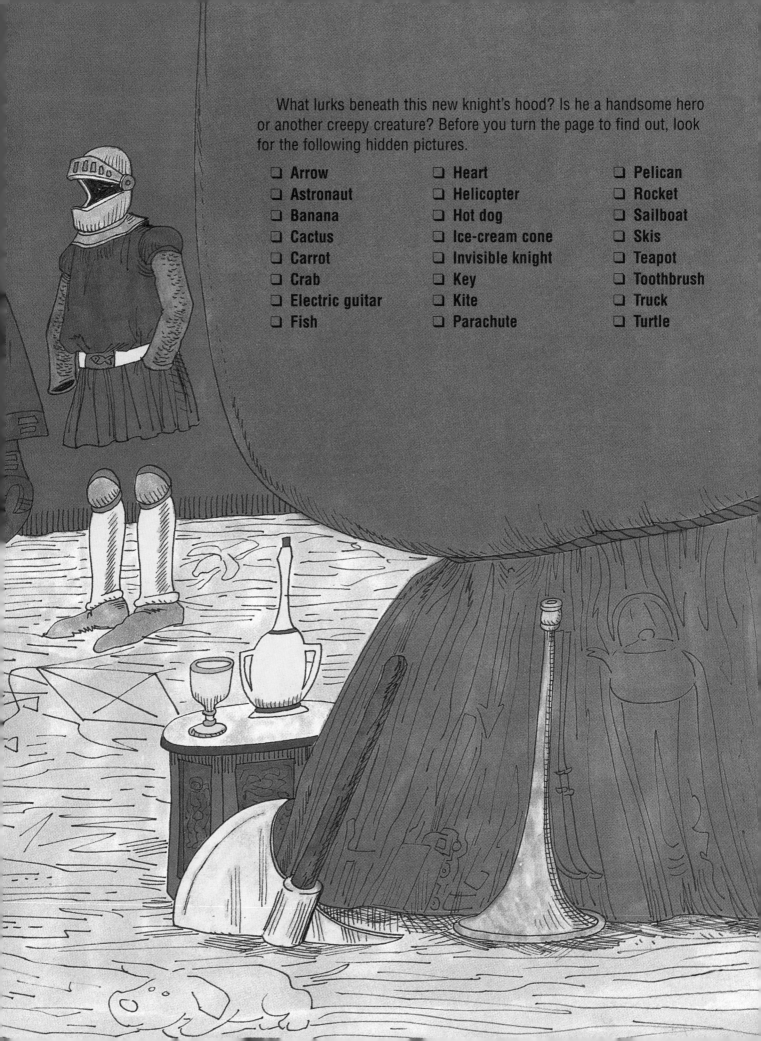

What lurks beneath this new knight's hood? Is he a handsome hero or another creepy creature? Before you turn the page to find out, look for the following hidden pictures.

❑ Arrow
❑ Astronaut
❑ Banana
❑ Cactus
❑ Carrot
❑ Crab
❑ Electric guitar
❑ Fish

❑ Heart
❑ Helicopter
❑ Hot dog
❑ Ice-cream cone
❑ Invisible knight
❑ Key
❑ Kite
❑ Parachute

❑ Pelican
❑ Rocket
❑ Sailboat
❑ Skis
❑ Teapot
❑ Toothbrush
❑ Truck
❑ Turtle

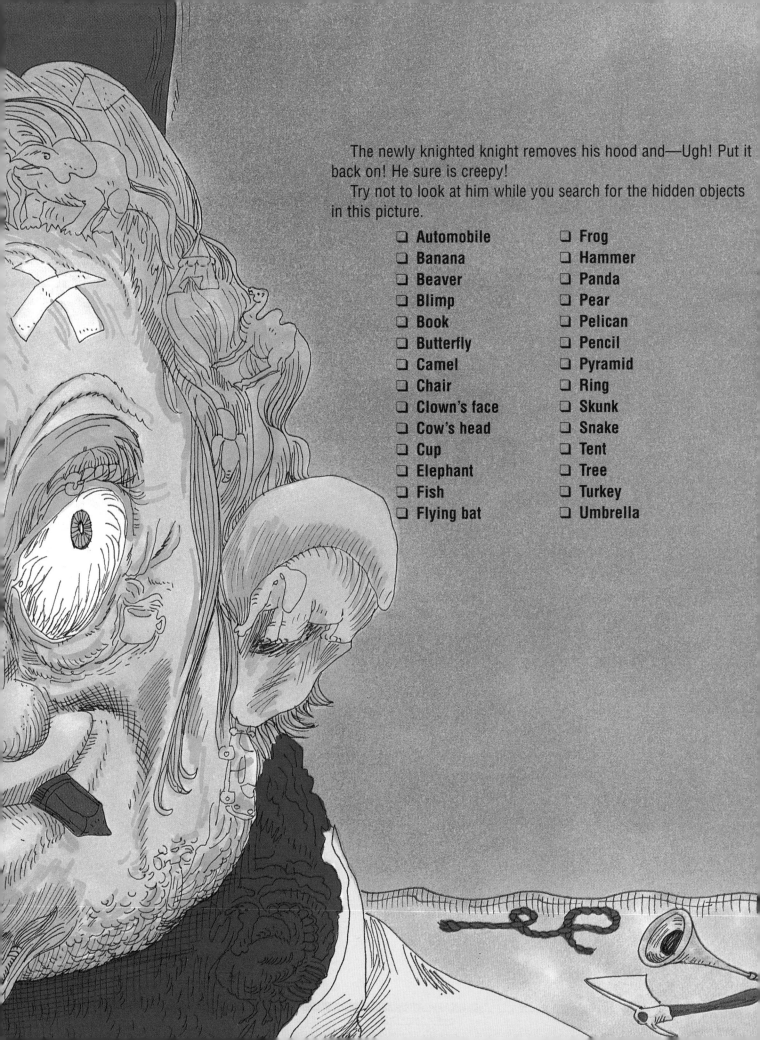

The newly knighted knight removes his hood and—Ugh! Put it back on! He sure is creepy!

Try not to look at him while you search for the hidden objects in this picture.

- ❏ **Automobile**
- ❏ **Banana**
- ❏ **Beaver**
- ❏ **Blimp**
- ❏ **Book**
- ❏ **Butterfly**
- ❏ **Camel**
- ❏ **Chair**
- ❏ **Clown's face**
- ❏ **Cow's head**
- ❏ **Cup**
- ❏ **Elephant**
- ❏ **Fish**
- ❏ **Flying bat**
- ❏ **Frog**
- ❏ **Hammer**
- ❏ **Panda**
- ❏ **Pear**
- ❏ **Pelican**
- ❏ **Pencil**
- ❏ **Pyramid**
- ❏ **Ring**
- ❏ **Skunk**
- ❏ **Snake**
- ❏ **Tent**
- ❏ **Tree**
- ❏ **Turkey**
- ❏ **Umbrella**

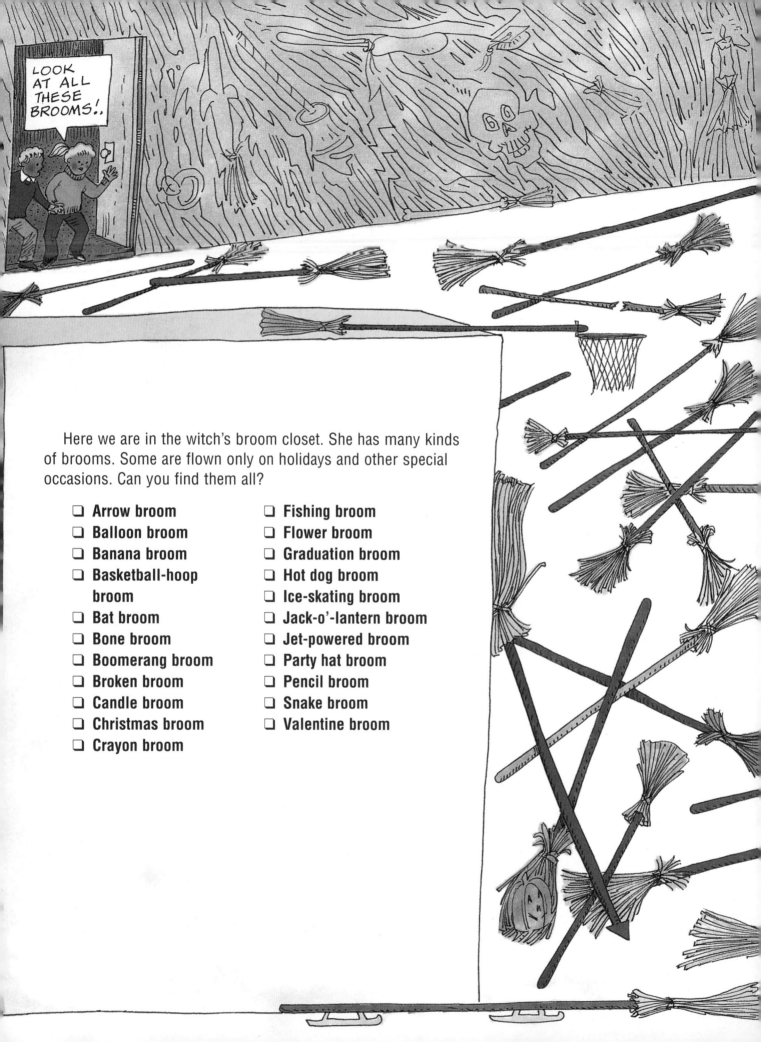

LOOK AT ALL THESE BROOMS!.

Here we are in the witch's broom closet. She has many kinds of brooms. Some are flown only on holidays and other special occasions. Can you find them all?

- ❏ Arrow broom
- ❏ Balloon broom
- ❏ Banana broom
- ❏ Basketball-hoop broom
- ❏ Bat broom
- ❏ Bone broom
- ❏ Boomerang broom
- ❏ Broken broom
- ❏ Candle broom
- ❏ Christmas broom
- ❏ Crayon broom
- ❏ Fishing broom
- ❏ Flower broom
- ❏ Graduation broom
- ❏ Hot dog broom
- ❏ Ice-skating broom
- ❏ Jack-o'-lantern broom
- ❏ Jet-powered broom
- ❏ Party hat broom
- ❏ Pencil broom
- ❏ Snake broom
- ❏ Valentine broom

Through a hole in the wall, our friends take a peek at Wizard Merlin as he creates nasty nightmares.

Peek carefully at this picture and find the following hidden objects.

- ❏ Airplane
- ❏ Apple
- ❏ Arrow
- ❏ Axe
- ❏ Bat
- ❏ Drum
- ❏ Elephant's head
- ❏ Football
- ❏ Ghost
- ❏ Gorilla
- ❏ Hearts (2)
- ❏ Helicopter
- ❏ Horse's head
- ❏ Ice-cream cone
- ❏ Kite
- ❏ Lion's face
- ❏ Lizard
- ❏ Magnet
- ❏ Mask
- ❏ Mouse
- ❏ Mushroom
- ❏ Octopus
- ❏ Owl
- ❏ Paintbrush
- ❏ Shark
- ❏ Skull
- ❏ Snake
- ❏ Top hat
- ❏ Toucan
- ❏ Windmill

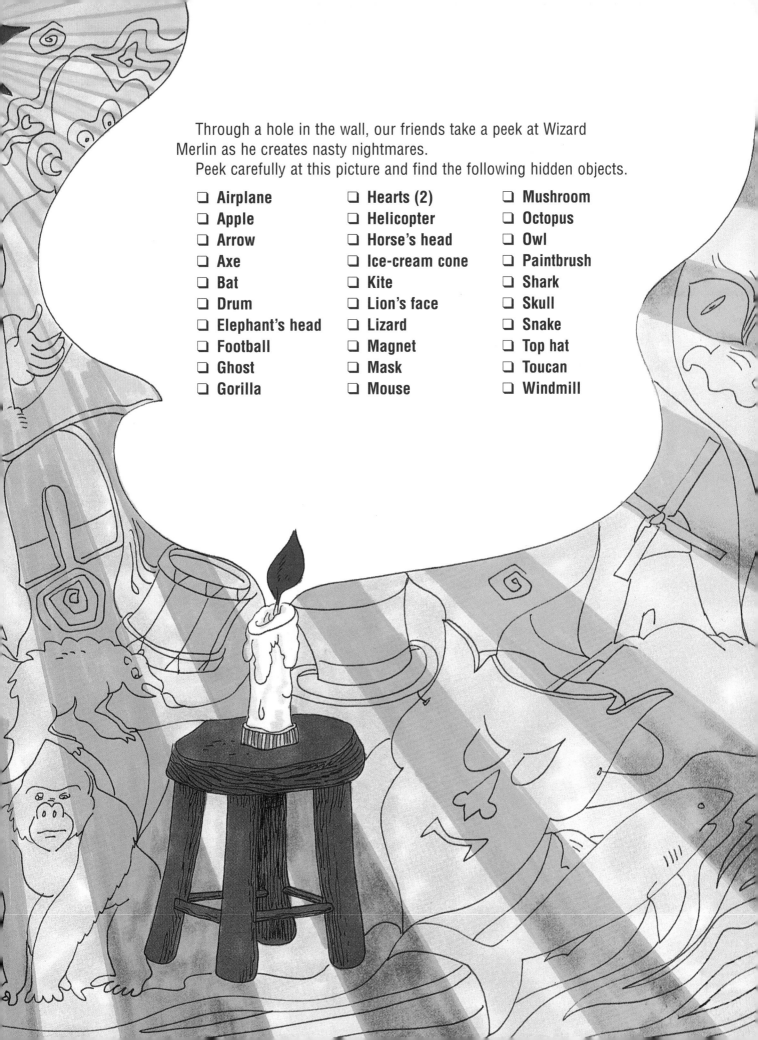

Surprise! Our fearless friends have been invited to a party in their honor. Looks like they are having a creepy, crazy good time!

You can join in the fun by finding the following hidden pictures.

- Arrows (2)
- Bottle
- Cup
- Fish
- Flower
- Flying bat
- Fork
- Ghosts (2)
- Hot dog
- Ice skate
- Key
- Kite
- Lightbulb
- Mitten
- Musical notes (2)
- Ponoil
- Penguin
- Piggy bank
- Pinwheel
- Rocket
- Rocking chair
- Roller skate
- Seal
- Sock
- Spoon
- Toothbrush

I WAS CROWNED PRINCE!

Congratulations! You have survived Creepy Castle! But what crazy gifts have our friends brought home?

See if you can find these peculiar presents hidden in the picture below.

- ❏ Barbell
- ❏ Broken clock
- ❏ Cactus
- ❏ Dog
- ❏ Fire hydrant
- ❏ Fountain
- ❏ Heart
- ❏ Ice-cream cone
- ❏ Key
- ❏ Kite
- ❏ Pirate
- ❏ Sailboat
- ❏ Television
- ❏ Tennis racket
- ❏ Tire
- ❏ Yo-yo

Christopher Columbus was born in Genoa, Italy, in 1451.

FIND BABY CHRISTOPHER BEING DELIVERED, AND THESE FUN ITEMS:

- ❏ Anchor
- ❏ Balcony
- ❏ Balloon
- ❏ Banana peel
- ❏ Broken chair
- ❏ Broom
- ❏ Candle
- ❏ Cat
- ❏ Cow
- ❏ Dog
- ❏ Flowerpot
- ❏ Green bird
- ❏ Hearts (2)
- ❏ Jester
- ❏ Kite
- ❏ Laundry
- ❏ Mouse
- ❏ Oar
- ❏ Plate
- ❏ Propeller
- ❏ Rabbits (2)
- ❏ Soccer ball
- ❏ Telescope
- ❏ Top hat
- ❏ Trunk
- ❏ TV antenna

Has the girl done her homework?
What is for sale?

When Columbus was young, some people believed that ships fell off the world's edge and into the mouths of giant sea creatures.

FIND COLUMBUS AT THE STORY-TELLING SCENE, AND THESE FUN ITEMS:

☐ Apple
☐ Arrow
☐ Ball
☐ Candle
☐ Chef
☐ Crocodile
☐ Dogs (2)
☐ Earmuffs
☐ Feather
☐ Fish (3)
☐ Flowerpot
☐ Flying bat
☐ Goggles
☐ Ice-cream cone
☐ Musician
☐ Paintbrush
☐ Pie
☐ Pot
☐ Roller skater
☐ Screwdriver
☐ Snowman
☐ Spoon
☐ Squirrel
☐ Sword

Who is Uncle Zeke?
What is Alma doing?

Christopher Columbus was the oldest of five children.

FIND COLUMBUS AS A YOUTH AT HIS FATHER'S WORKPLACE, AND THESE FUN ITEMS:

- ❏ Bottle
- ❏ Carrot
- ❏ Clothespin
- ❏ Comb
- ❏ Crayon
- ❏ Fish
- ❏ Flower
- ❏ Football
- ❏ Grapes
- ❏ Hammer
- ❏ Hearts (4)
- ❏ Horse
- ❏ Hourglass
- ❏ Ice skate
- ❏ Keys (3)
- ❏ Mice (4)
- ❏ Moth
- ❏ Necktie
- ❏ Pirate
- ❏ Ring
- ❏ Saw
- ❏ Scissors
- ❏ Sheep (2)
- ❏ Toothbrush
- ❏ Turtle
- ❏ Yo-yo

What was Christopher's father's occupation? Who is late?

The explorer Columbus admired most was Marco Polo.

FIND COLUMBUS AS HE DAYDREAMS, AND THESE FUN ITEMS:

- ☐ Apple
- ☐ Arrow
- ☐ Baseball cap
- ☐ Bell
- ☐ Car
- ☐ Elephant
- ☐ Feather
- ☐ Fish
- ☐ Flower
- ☐ Ghost
- ☐ Ice-cream cone
- ☐ Jack-in-the-box
- ☐ Jack-o'-lantern
- ☐ Kite
- ☐ Lion
- ☐ Mouse
- ☐ Net
- ☐ Owl
- ☐ Paintbrush
- ☐ Pear
- ☐ Rabbit
- ☐ Ship
- ☐ Skull
- ☐ Stars (5)
- ☐ Tepee
- ☐ Umbrella

How long was Marco Polo's stay?
What was the name of the emperor?

Columbus arrived in Portugal after a ship that he was on sank after an attack by the French.

FIND COLUMBUS AMONG THE SHIP-WRECKED SAILORS, AND THESE FUN ITEMS:

- ☐ Accordion
- ☐ Arrow
- ☐ Bathtub
- ☐ Beach ball
- ☐ Birdbath
- ☐ Bone
- ☐ Books (4)
- ☐ Broom
- ☐ Crayon
- ☐ Cup
- ☐ Drums (2)
- ☐ Envelope
- ☐ Fire hydrants (2)
- ☐ Fishbowl
- ☐ Football
- ☐ Kite
- ☐ Octopus
- ☐ Paper airplane
- ☐ Periscope
- ☐ Pie
- ☐ Pizza
- ☐ Shark fins (3)
- ☐ Top hat
- ☐ Treasure chest

Where was the ship going? To what city will Columbus go next?

Columbus wanted to find the shortest route to the Indies by sailing west from Portugal, instead of sailing east.

FIND COLUMBUS IN THE TROLL'S TOLL LINE, AND THESE FUN ITEMS:

- ☐ **Alligators (2)**
- ☐ **Apple**
- ☐ **Artist**
- ☐ **Banana peel**
- ☐ **Duck**
- ☐ **Elephant**
- ☐ **Flying bat**
- ☐ **Genie and his lamp**
- ☐ **Ice skates (5)**
- ☐ **Kangaroo**
- ☐ **Lost boot**
- ☐ **Rabbit**
- ☐ **Red wagon**
- ☐ **Roller skater**
- ☐ **Sacks (5)**
- ☐ **Sailboat**
- ☐ **Schoolbags (2)**
- ☐ **Ship in a bottle**
- ☐ **Skateboard**
- ☐ **Skier**
- ☐ **Snowman**
- ☐ **Telescope**
- ☐ **Turtles (2)**
- ☐ **Umbrella**
- ☐ **Walking stick**
- ☐ **Watering can**

Who is collecting the tolls?
What is for sale?

Portugal's rulers would not pay for Columbus's plan to sail to the Indies.

FIND COLUMBUS IN THE KING'S COURT, AND THESE FUN ITEMS:

- ❑ Axe
- ❑ Bears (2)
- ❑ Bowling ball
- ❑ Broom
- ❑ Cactus
- ❑ Camel
- ❑ Candles (2)
- ❑ Chef's hat
- ❑ Fish (2)
- ❑ Football
- ❑ Frog
- ❑ Hockey stick
- ❑ Hot dog
- ❑ Ice skate
- ❑ Igloo
- ❑ Lion
- ❑ Medal
- ❑ Paintbrush
- ❑ Pen
- ❑ Shopping bag
- ❑ Spoon
- ❑ Star
- ❑ Train
- ❑ Truck
- ❑ Turtle
- ❑ Yo-yo
- ❑ Zipper

How many jokes does the jester have?
Who was a prince?

Columbus appealed to Spain's Queen Isabella and King Ferdinand for money to begin his journey. Eventually, the queen and royal treasurer gave him the funds.

FIND COLUMBUS IN SPAIN, AND THESE FUN ITEMS:

- ☐ Alien creature
- ☐ Anchor
- ☐ Baseball
- ☐ Candles (3)
- ☐ Count Dracula
- ☐ Crowns (4)
- ☐ Cups (2)
- ☐ Dart
- ☐ Feather
- ☐ Fish (2)
- ☐ Frogs (2)
- ☐ Ghost
- ☐ Giraffe
- ☐ Gold coin
- ☐ Heart
- ☐ Hot dog
- ☐ Mice (2)
- ☐ Paintbrush
- ☐ Pig
- ☐ Rabbit
- ☐ Seal
- ☐ Ship
- ☐ Snowman
- ☐ Telescope
- ☐ Worm

Who is Harold?
Who is going to shave?

Christopher Columbus set sail on August 3, 1492, with three ships—the *Niña*, the *Pinta*, and the *Santa María*.

FIND COLUMBUS WITH HIS SHIPS, AND THESE FUN ITEMS:

- ❏ Anchor
- ❏ Barrel of monkeys
- ❏ Basket
- ❏ Black bird
- ❏ Bottles (2)
- ❏ Cactus
- ❏ Candle
- ❏ Coffeepot
- ❏ Football
- ❏ Hamburgers (2)
- ❏ Hammer
- ❏ Helmet
- ❏ Lost boot
- ❏ Lunch box
- ❏ Mermaid
- ❏ Pig
- ❏ Pink fish (3)
- ❏ Pumpkin
- ❏ Rabbit
- ❏ Rat
- ❏ Shipwrecked sailor
- ❏ Television
- ❏ Tires (2)
- ❏ Unicorn
- ❏ Worm
- ❏ Would-be surfer

On which ship is Columbus sailing? Which is the smallest?

In October 1492, Columbus reached San Salvador, an island in the Bahamas.

FIND COLUMBUS ON THIS TROPICAL ISLAND IN THE NEW WORLD, AND THESE FUN ITEMS:

- ☐ Banana peel
- ☐ Book
- ☐ Clothespin
- ☐ Clown
- ☐ Dog
- ☐ Duck
- ☐ Feather
- ☐ Football
- ☐ Ghost
- ☐ Ice skates
- ☐ Kite
- ☐ Lizard
- ☐ Lost mitten
- ☐ Mice (2)
- ☐ Oars (6)
- ☐ Painted egg
- ☐ Pencil
- ☐ Pig
- ☐ Rabbit
- ☐ Scarecrow
- ☐ Seesaw
- ☐ Snail
- ☐ Snake
- ☐ Stars (3)
- ☐ Train engine
- ☐ Turtle
- ☐ Wooden leg

Who wants a cracker?
Who is all wet?

Upon Columbus's return, he was named Admiral of the Ocean Sea and Viceroy of the Indies. On September 25, 1493, he set sail on his second journey to the New World, with 17 ships and about 1,000 men.

FIND COLUMBUS AS THE SHIPS SET SAIL, AND THESE FUN ITEMS:

- ❏ Arrow
- ❏ Baseball bat
- ❏ Birds (2)
- ❏ Broom
- ❏ Camel
- ❏ Candle
- ❏ Cooking pot
- ❏ Fish (3)
- ❏ Flying bat
- ❏ Fork
- ❏ Ghost
- ❏ Heart
- ❏ Mouse
- ❏ Pen
- ❏ Quarter moon
- ❏ Seal
- ❏ Snowman
- ❏ Star
- ❏ Tent
- ❏ Toothbrush
- ❏ TV antenna
- ❏ Upside-down tree

How many ships sailed this time?
Who did not escape from the zoo?

The first lesson of the day is arithmetic. But what's wrong here? Search for and find at least 12 things that are wrong in this classroom.

The annual school play is scheduled to begin in a few days. However, there are a few things wrong with this full-dress rehearsal. Look for exactly <u>10</u> of them.

The Arts and Crafts Club is meeting in room 221. Everything is under control—or is it? Find at least 12 things that are out of control and wrong with this picture.

Today is the day of the big test. Exams aren't really that difficult if you've studied for them. If you haven't, you'll have many wrong answers. Can you find <u>12</u> things that are wrong here?

This year, the class trip is to Prehistoric Times Amusement Park. The dinosaur slide looks like fun! Find at least 15 things wrong with this picture.

Another week of school has ended. Some students are staying for after-school activities. Before the rest leave for home, there are at least 18 wrong things here for you to find.

The children have discovered a real haunted house! Who's going to be brave enough to enter? You'll find out on the next page. But first, what's wrong here? At least 15 things. Can you find them?

All the children follow Bob and Bobbie into the house. In the living room they see 13 ghosts! First find them. Then try to find at least 6 things that are wrong with this picture.

TICK-TOCK-TICK-TOCK!

CAP

A giant skeleton drops in on the kids! Every scared one of them scrambles to get out. Before they do, search for and find at least 10 things that are wrong with this picture.

The friendly fiends ask the children to help them fix and clean the haunted house. Look at the mess in this room and find at least <u>10</u> things that are wrong.

The house is soon fixed, cleaned, and painted, both inside and out. It looks so good that no one will ever believe it was a genuine haunted house. We know better! But there are still at least <u>10</u> wrong things here for you to find.

The first stop is the Wacky Little Schoolhouse. Come inside and help find at least <u>10</u> things that are wrong here.

The flume ride is almost ready to go—except for a few things that are wrong. Can you find exactly 12 things that are wrong with this picture?

No amusement park is complete without its very own wacky circus. How many wrong things can you find here?

Have your tickets ready, please! The Toot-Toot train ride has begun. Along the way, look for and find at least 18 things that are wrong with this picture.

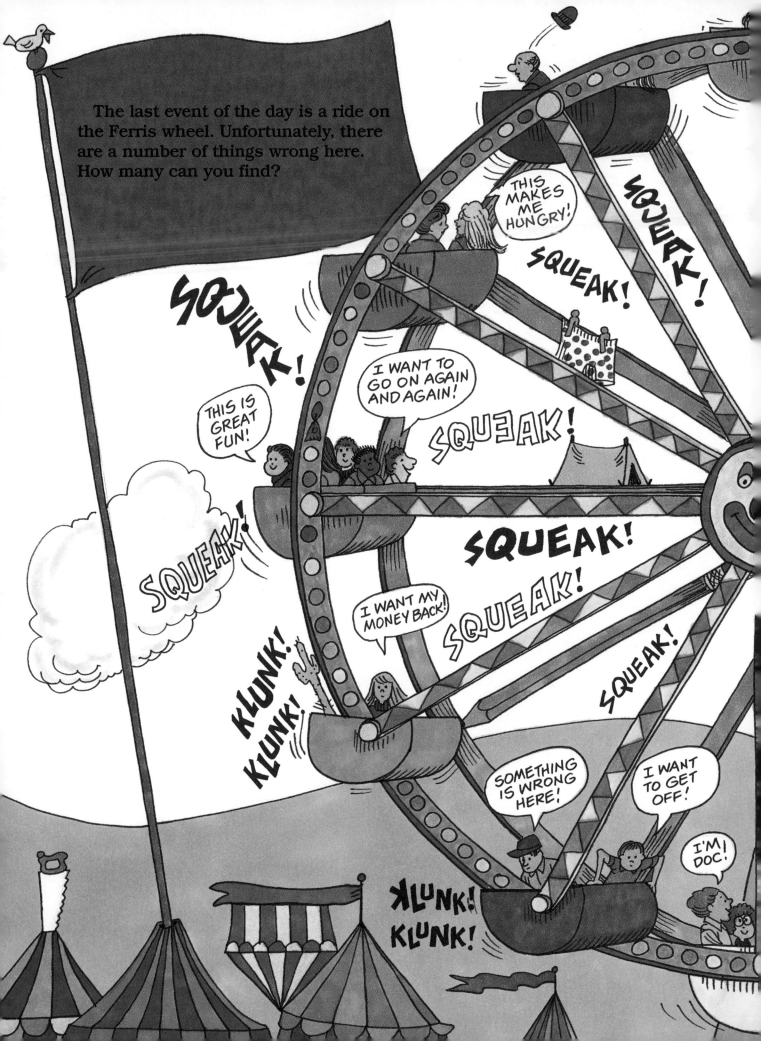

The last event of the day is a ride on the Ferris wheel. Unfortunately, there are a number of things wrong here. How many can you find?

It's movie time! Let's all go see our favorite flick! But first, find at least 12 things that are wrong with this picture.

The Ninjas are getting ready to do battle on the big screen—and you are seeing it! Can you also see 10 things that are wrong with this picture?

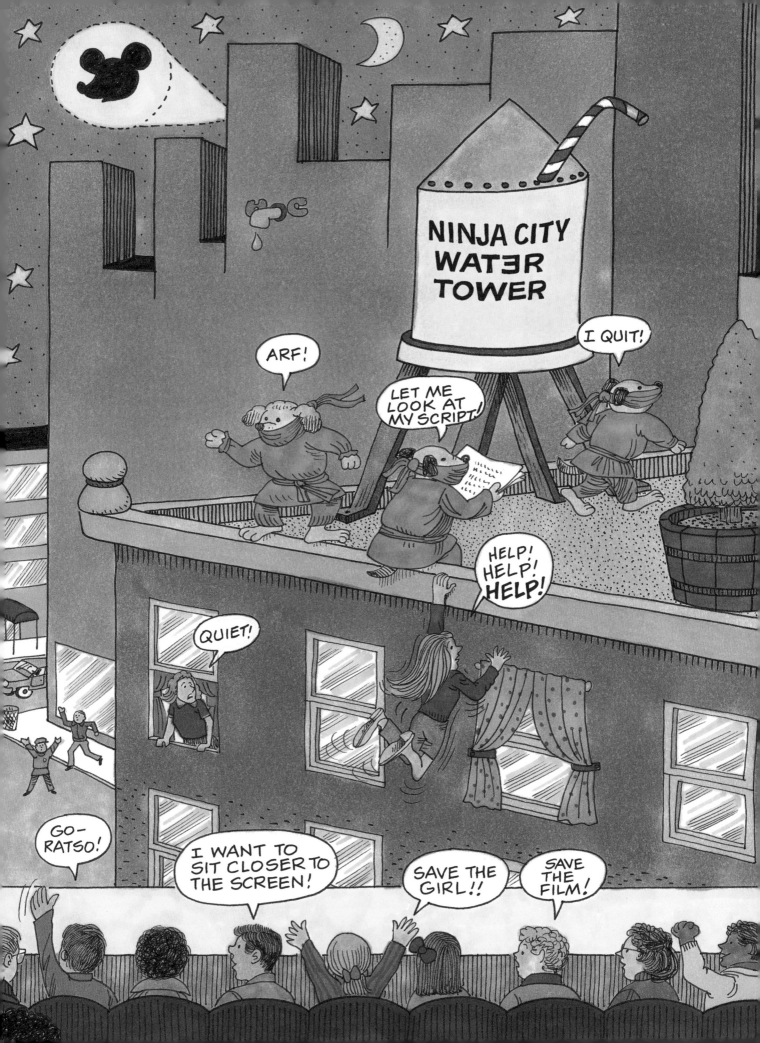

The great detective Sheerluck Homes is featured in his 249th movie. The old boy is searching for that famous criminal, Professor Moranutty. What he *should* be searching for is all the things that are wrong in this picture. How many can you find?

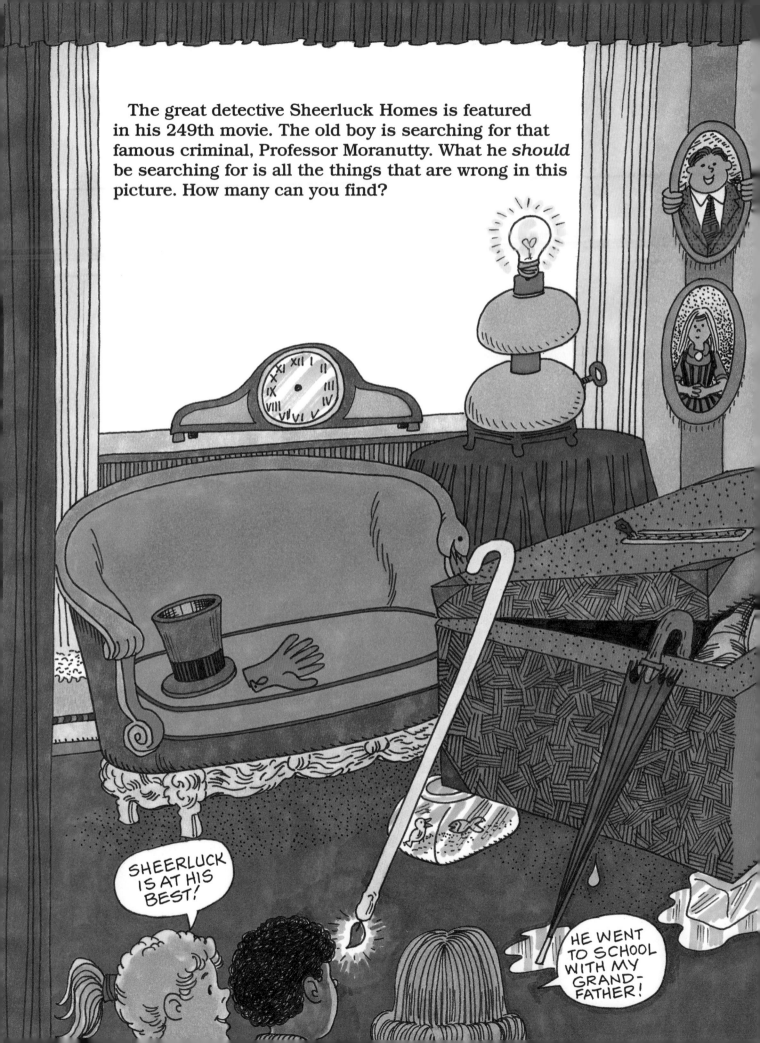

SHEERLUCK IS AT HIS BEST!

HE WENT TO SCHOOL WITH MY GRAND-FATHER!

In this movie, Robin Hood and Little John are fighting over the right to cross the log bridge first. Look for and find at least 15 things wrong with this picture.

This old-time silent movie has many things wrong with it. Can you find at least <u>18</u>?

Wow! What a crazy maze of daisies!

FIND BUNNY HONEY IN THIS DAISY MAZE, AND THESE FUN ITEMS:

- ❏ **Airplane**
- ❏ **Apple**
- ❏ **Arrow**
- ❏ **Balloon**
- ❏ **Baseball bat**
- ❏ **Basket**
- ❏ **Bee**
- ❏ **Bone**
- ❏ **Camel**
- ❏ **Cap**
- ❏ **Carrot**
- ❏ **Clown**
- ❏ **Elephant**
- ❏ **Fish (2)**
- ❏ **Frog**
- ❏ **Helicopter**
- ❏ **Igloo**
- ❏ **Monster**
- ❏ **Pencil**
- ❏ **Ring**
- ❏ **Schoolbag**
- ❏ **Shovel**
- ❏ **Snail**
- ❏ **Snake**
- ❏ **Snowman**
- ❏ **Sock**
- ❏ **Squirrel**
- ❏ **Sunglasses**
- ❏ **Train engine**
- ❏ **Violin**